This book belongs to

www.beyondthemoon.org

Beyond the Moon wants to bring about **lasting and heartwarming memories** and a **good feeling**, on the one hand, to the families with a sick child enjoying a carefree vacation and, on the other, to the sponsors and partners supporting our charity.

OUR VISION

Beyond the Moon is of the opinion that every child should get the chance to be a child and enjoy life. We strongly believe that a relaxing vacation is a fundamental right for everyone, especially for families with a sick child. A sick child, who today can relax and have fun with his family, will better fight against the disease tomorrow. A Beyond the Moon vacation gives hope, energy and joy and helps strengthen the family ties.

OUR MISSION

Beyond the Moon offers families with a seriously ill child the opportunity to enjoy a memorable, cost-free vacation in a child-friendly environment and to spend carefree quality time together, far away from hospitals and treatments.

OUR LOGO

The MOON in our logo symbolises the carefree family vacation and brightens up the often dark and painful days of these families. The joyful holiday memories will be cherished forever and reach BEYOND their expectations and dreams. We make every effort to ensure that the Beyond the Moon vacation provides them with lifelong memories - especially should the sick child pass away.

This book has been dedicated to all the families who devote themselves to lovingly support and care for their sick child. By buying this book you help such families enjoy a well deserved Beyond the Moon holiday. All proceeds go to Beyond the Moon.

MY SPECIAL

Family Holiday

Where does the time go,

I really just don't know.

The year is flying by

and we're forever on the go.

Everybody is so busy,

there is always something on.

Before we know it,

another year has gone.

I can't wait for our family holiday
and to go away.
Somewhere we can rest, have fun
and of course play.
I wonder where we'll holiday this year
and when will we go.
I get so excited,
that I really need to know.

It's such a big adventure

planning for a trip.

We could be in a car, aeroplane

or sail on a ship.

The world is such a big place,

there are so many places to visit.

How many holidays can you go on,

I don't think there's a limit.

Mum and dad have decided this year,

we will all *go* abroad.

I was so happy,

I started to dance and applaud.

One day we went shopping

and bought some holiday gear.

I'm now counting down the sleeps

as our holiday gets near.

The suitcases are out

and I hope they can all fit in the car.

It looks like there's a lot to take,

when you're travelling so far.

I just did not realise

there was so much to pack.

I hope the suitcases aren't too heavy,

and dad doesn't hurt his back.

We wake up early

and are packed and ready to go.

Before you know we're near the airport,

but traffic is slow.

'Are we there yet?' I ask one more time,

bursting for a wee.

'Not long to go' I'm told,

'you just wait and see.'

The airport is so big

and such a busy place.

We're all checked in

and I say bye to my case.

We go through security

and I take in all the sights.

So many people travelling,

there must be lots of flights.

Flying on a plane is like

being on big bus and no big deal.

Apart from you're in the sky

and might even get a meal.

I watch some movies on the plane,

while dad has a nap.

You can even see where you're flying,

on a big bright map.

We arrive at the hotel

and it's such a great place.

I'm so happy that I can't

take the smile off my face.

The hotel is where we are

going to stay and to sleep.

I'm going to make the most of our holiday,

I'm sure it wasn't cheap.

We spend time on the beach

and even in the sea.

We're all having such fun,

though mum misses a good cup of tea.

I made lots of sand castles,

with my bucket and spade.

It was so much fun playing on the beach and

seeing footprints that I made.

The hotel pool was really

warm and great.

We tried to make sure we got

there early and never late.

The sun was out most days

and I think I might have a tan.

I love our family holiday,

which must make me a fan.

Before you know, it was time

to come home and say farewells.

We packed all our things,

I even remembered my shells.

After landing back at the airport

we were feeling a little sad.

But when we got home though,

we were all really glad.

I thanked mum and dad for our holiday,

it was such a fun treat.

Quality family time and a

chance to put up your feet.

It's so nice to sleep in my own bed

and remember our holiday by the sea.

I can't wait for our next one,

wherever it may be.

The End

24008281R00020

Printed in Great Britain
by Amazon